D1358317

# HEY!

We've got a problem. Inside this book there's a story about lots of different monsters. Big ones, small ones, smelly ones... but this book has no pictures!

We need an illustrator to help us finish this book.

Hello! **Stephanie** here. I'm an artist, and I live in Thailand. I love to draw with bright colors! I've started some pictures in this book, but I need your help to finish them! Do you think you can illustrate this entire book?

**YES**     **NO**

I'M AN ARTIST

Whoa, hang on! Really?

I agree, you've got this!

**Listen, I know you can do this.
What's holding you back? Let me give you
a few tips, from one illustrator to another:**

1. Don't worry about what you *think* your
   picture should look like. Just let yourself
   draw the way you want to.

2. Try not to compare your drawings to others.
   No one can draw the same way you can!

3. If you can't think of something to draw,
   pick a shape and turn it into a picture.
   Maybe you will invent something new!

So, are you ready to illustrate your own book?

YES     NO

LET'S GO ➡

I'm not taking no for an answer...

Not so fast...

# PRACTICE YOUR PEN SKILLS.

Trace...

# COLLECT IDEAS & DO RESEARCH

Try copying this drawing!

**monster**

**spotty**

**smelly**

**These are some of the words that you will illustrate in this book. Look up what these words mean, and practice drawing them here!**

far

near

curly

Things that are close to us look bigger. Make your drawing take up the whole space.

# BOOK PLANNER

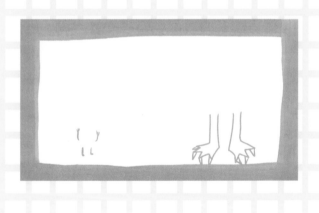

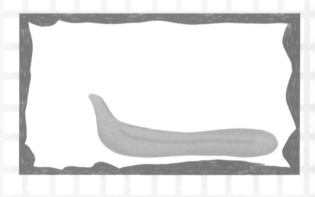

These are all the pages in your book. Read the story first, then use this planner to sketch out your drawings for each page. It doesn't have to be perfect, just try some ideas.

Great job!
You're ready
to make your
own book.

# LET'S GO ➡

# MONSTER SMALL,
# MONSTER BIG!

Illustrated by:

_____

(you!)

Monster **small**, monster **big**,

monster in a **curly** wig!

Finish these monsters!

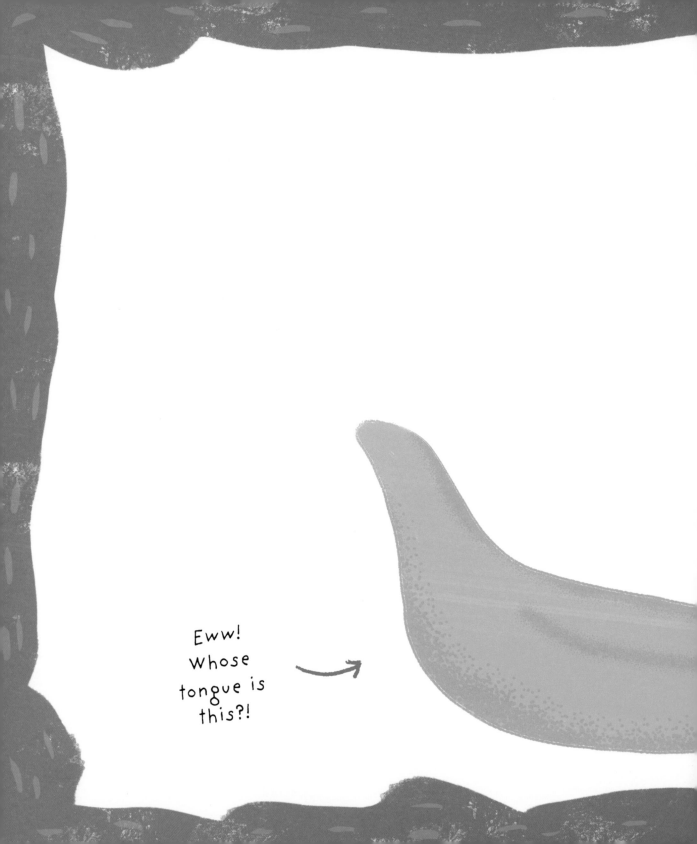

Eww! Whose tongue is this?!

Monster **old**, monster **young**,

monster with a long, green **tongue**!

Monster **near**, monster **far**,

monster laughing har! **har! har!**

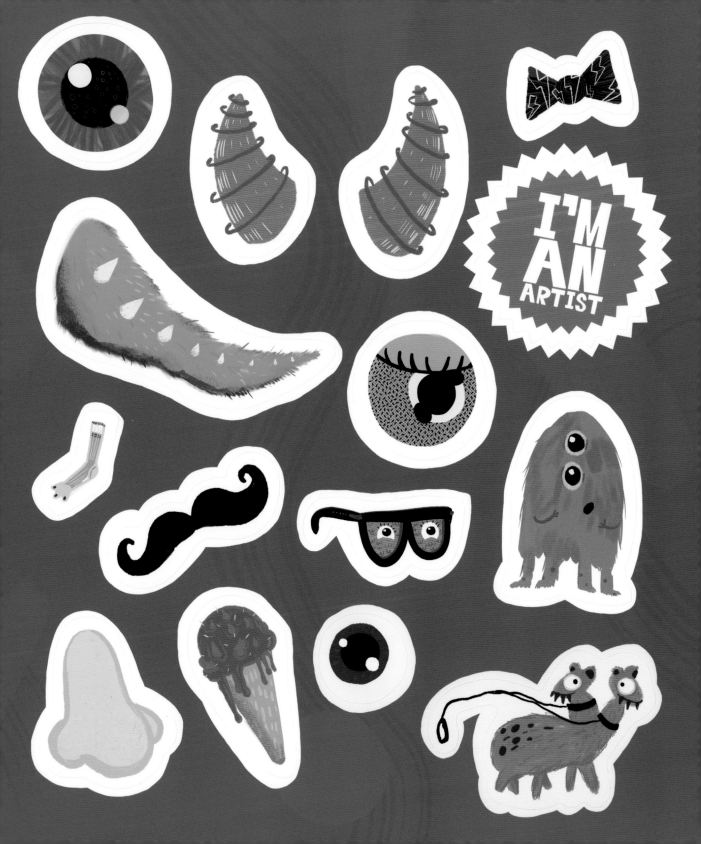

I'M AN ARTIST

A faraway monster will look very small in the distance. Can you draw it?

Monster **wet**, monster **dry**,

monster with a **spotty** tie!

Draw some rain!
Or is something
else making the
monster wet?

# Monster **weak,**

## monster **strong...**

... smelly monster,

don't stay **long!**

Can you imagine
what a stinky
smell might look
like? How would
you draw it?

Monster **round**, monster **square**...

Monster wearing underwear!

Who is
wearing
underwear?

# Monsters **many...**

How many
monsters can
you count?

# Monsters **few...**

Turn all the
shapes into
monsters!

# Monsters coming after **you!**

How will you
get away?!

**A minute later...**

This page is
all yours! What
happens next?
Do you outsmart
the monsters?

# THE END

## (Not!)

**Congratulations!** You've done an **amazing job** of illustrating this book. But it's not over yet. Now that you have made your very own book, you can **display it** somewhere, give it to someone as a present, or **make more books** and set up a bookshop in your bedroom! Whatever you do, be sure to **share your work** with the world because your creativity will **inspire others.** It's been great working with you!

# ILLUSTRATE THIS BOOK!

## What's your next project?

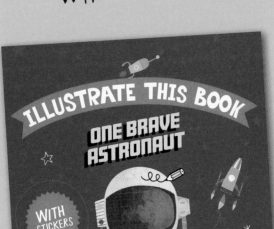

ILLUSTRATE THIS BOOK
**ONE BRAVE ASTRONAUT**

WITH STICKERS

Written by Kitty Harrison and illustrated by _____ (you!)

Ben Hawkes and _____

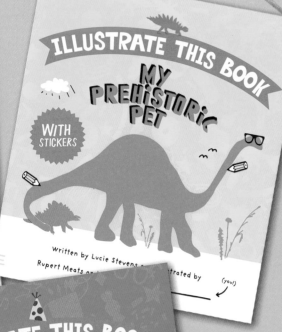

ILLUSTRATE THIS BOOK
**MY PREHISTORIC PET**

WITH STICKERS

Written by Lucie Stevens and _____ illustrated by _____ (you!)

Rupert Meats an _____

ILLUSTRATE THIS BOOK
**THE UNICORN PARTY**

WITH STICKERS

Written by Kitty Harrison and illustrated by

Cris Martin and _____

# Learning Guide

Hi, grown-ups!

The ILLUSTRATE THIS BOOK series empowers children to explore literacy through drawing.

We know that drawing is a powerful learning tool. It can help children build confidence and strengthen visual literacies while supporting them to reach their reading and writing milestones.

As your child completes this book they will use their own ingenuity to develop three crucial elements of literacy:

- Vocabulary
- Reading comprehension
- Visual literacy

You may find that your child needs support for the practice and research pages at the start of the book. That's a great way for you to collaborate and help them plan.

On the story pages, encourage them to take the lead and come up with ideas for illustrating the pages. This is where their imaginations can shine.

Don't be afraid to draw, too. We often hear adults say, "I can't draw!" But there is no right or wrong with art. If you sketch a chicken and it looks like a frog, you've invented a new animal. That's your creativity at work.